Who Am I?

Written by Frank Friedmann

Illustrated by Joe McCormick

"Finally, a book for children has been written which teaches our identity in Christ! *Who Am I?* makes it plain and simple for small children to understand this life transforming truth. Every Christian parent in America needs to read this book with their children!"

Steve McVey
President, Grace Walk Ministries
Atlanta, Georgia

For worldwide distribution. Printed in Mexico.
Published by Companion Press, an imprint of Genesis Communications, Inc., P.O. Box 91011, Mobile, AL 36691
Distributed by Streamwood Distribution, 1-888-670-7463, E-mail: GenesisCom@aol.com
Call for a complete catalog of products distributed by Streamwood Distribution.

ISBN# 1-58169-018-5

DEDICATION

This book is dedicated to the five children of God in my life: Janet, Les-Leigh, Benjamin, Morgan and Avery. Thank you for the life we share in Jesus.

ACKNOWLEDGEMENTS

A special thank you to Matt and Holly Boardman, Paul and Kim Byrd, David and Christine Eberhardt, Al and Carol Hanson, and Michael and Catherine Word. Without you, this project would not have come to pass. Bless you!

I have a name, and I know my name.

But who am I?

I can play with toys.
Does that mean I'm a toy?

No—of course not! I can play with toys, but that's not who I am. So who am I?

I can swim like a fish.
Does that mean I'm a fish?

No—of course not! I can swim like a fish,
but that's not who I am. So who am I?

I can bark like a dog.
Does that mean I'm a dog?

No—of course not! I can bark like a dog, but
that's not who I am. So who am I?

I can do good things like play with my brother or clean my room. Does that mean I'm good?

No—of course not! I can do good things, but that's not who I am. So who am I?

I can do bad things, like lying or stealing. Does that mean I'm bad?

No—of course not! I can do bad things, but that's not who I am. So who am I?

God said I became His child when I believed that Jesus died for my sins and rose again!

And that means...

It's not what I DO that makes me who I am.
It's what GOD SAYS that makes me who I am!

And that means...

When I play with my toys,
I'm God's child who plays with my toys.

And...

When I swim like a fish,
I'm God's child who swims like a fish.

And...

When I bark like a dog,
I'm God's child who barks like a dog.

And...

When I do good things,
I'm God's child who does good things.

But...

What about when I do bad things?

When I do bad things, I'm God's child
who does bad things. And that means...

I'm not acting like God's child,
and that makes me sad.

It makes God sad, too. But...

God loves me and has forgiven me. He says that I'm His child, and I'll always be His child.

That's who I am! I'M GOD'S FORGIVEN CHILD!

Father, thank you for making me who I am.

Thank you for sending Jesus so that I could become Your child. I love You. Amen!

"Behold, what manner of love
the Father has bestowed upon us,
that we should be called the children
of God; AND SUCH WE ARE!"

I John 3:1

Frank Friedmann is the pastor of Quail Ridge Bible Church in Baton Rouge, LA., where he lives with his wife Janet and their four children. He is also the author of another children's book, *I Was Wrong, But God Made Me Right,* available from: Living in Grace, 10051 Siegen Lane, Baton Rouge, LA 70810.
Voice mail: 1-800-484-2046 (Ext. #9506) • E-mail: QRBC@aol.com